CW00420129

The Story of
The Bowder Stone

Alan Smith

THE BOWDER STONE

The Bowder Stone is one of the most popular visitor attractions of the Lake District. For hundreds of years it has been the subject of awe, speculation and amazement. It is more than just a natural geological curiosity. An interesting history also surrounds the site. This booklet describes the Stone, relates its history as a tourist site over the last 200 years and explains the origin of this remarkable feature.

Seeing the Bowder Stone for the first time you are immediately struck by two things. First its sheer size and bulk. Measuring just over 18m in length and standing 8.18m in vertical height, it is far and away the biggest free-standing lump of rock in the Lake District. Second, and more distinctively, is the way it apparently balances on one corner in an almost gravity defying way. It has been likened most frequently to a stranded ship with its keel upturned, but more amusingly it has been described as:

'an enormous lady standing on tiptoe as if to convince us that she is a prima ballerina' (B. J. Bailey, Lakeland Walks and Legends 1981) or..

'a great lump of rock the size of a house, stranded like a petrified mammoth of the Ice Age'. (Molly Lefebure, The English Lake District 1964) or..

'perched on one corner like a performing elephant on one leg' (Norman Nicholson, Greater Lakeland, 1969).

JOSEPH POCKLINGTON (1736-1817)

In 1798 the land around the Bowder Stone was bought by a wealthy eccentric gentleman, Joseph Pocklington, whose antics locally earned him the name *'King Pocky '*. The second son of a Newark banker, Pocklington, after the death of his father in 1764, lived the uninterrupted life of a bachelor and gentleman. After early building ventures in Nottinghamshire he came to the Lake District in 1778, being one of the earliest pioneers to settle in the district for the beauty of the landscape, prefiguring what was to come in the Nineteenth Century. He bought Vicar's Island in Derwentwater, immediately changed its name to Pocklington's Island and proceeded to build a considerable mansion of his own design accompanied by a range of outrageous follies. His love of building became a mania. He kept lists of his works with precise costs, as well as producing his own architectural designs, topographical drawings and notes of his craftsmen. His tastes were reviled by contemporary commentators, but nevertheless his obsession with building and 'improving' the landscape continued. After his island mansion, he built a second large house in Portinscale near Keswick. In 1787 he purchased land at Barrow, near Ashness on the eastern shore of Derwentwater, where he constructed an even more lavish mansion with a number of ornamental features, including a major improvement to the waterfall making it into a cascade, leading him to call the property Barrow Cascade House. (now Derwentwater YHA).

In 1798 he 'set to work' on the Bowder Stone area, shrewdly aware that the stone had tourist potential. He seems to have cleared away most of the smaller loose material from around the foot of the Stone, erected some kind of fence around it and thus defined it as a clear free-standing feature emphasizing its perched nature. Additionally, he erected a mock hermitage or chapel, set up a druid stone and built Bowderstone Cottage. He installed a lady resident in the cottage to show visitors around. It was Pocklington who first erected a ladder enabling visitors to reach to the top of the Stone. He also enlarged a hole at the base of the stone towards the southern end, in order to allow his lady guide (for a small fee) to shake hands with visitors lying down on the other side of the precariously balanced stone, 'to improve their luck'.

Bowderstone Cottage, surrounded by the walls that once enclosed its gardens, remains intact today, still in good condition and now used as a climbing club hut. The druid stone stands as Pocklington erected it on the crag just south of the Stone.

Bowderstone Cottage

The Druid Stone and the Small Climbing Club Hut.

The ladder, now maintained by The National Trust, the present owners of the site, still enables visitors to reach the top. Any fence around it has long since disappeared. The present track up to the Stone from the road was in Pocklington's day the main road up Borrowdale. It is still just possible to see the hole beneath the Stone, although the loose stones on the ground now make it very difficult to access it and virtually impossible to shake hands with anyone on the other side.

The history of the hermitage or chapel is rather more obscure. The only remaining record is Pocklington's own engraving of the building, shown below. It depicts a gabled building with a Gothic bellcote, but square domestic windows and a porch with a semi-circular arch leading to a blank wall. It thus appears to have been a mock chapel, whether it was ever used in any way and how long it existed remains a mystery.

Pocklington's engraving of the now vanished Bowder Stone Chapel

It almost certainly stood where the small climbing club hut stands today. This is supported by William Green's drawing of the Stone (below), done probably around 1818. Most likely, the present small climbing club hut was built using the masonry from the chapel.

THE WEIGHT OF THE STONE

Joseph Pocklington, true to his meticulous nature, made measurements of the Stone and calculated its weight in 1799. In his personal notebook, which fortunately still exists, he made the following record.

Measure of Bowtherstone in
Borrowdale Cumberland ꝺ 9
The Length of the Stone is 62: 6
Perpendicular Hright———— 36: 0
Circumference. 89: 0
Contents of Solid Feet——— 23,000 :0
Weight of the above 1771 Tons X 13 Hun
Measure May 15 1799 by me J P.

He seems to have used the simple measurements of length, height and girth to calculate a figure for the volume of the stone (what he calls solid feet) and then by an arithmetical calculation to come up with the weight as 1771 tons and 13 hundredweights. His girth measurement of 89 feet appears to have been arrived at by passing a surveying chain through the hole at the base and then around the stone.

As early as 1831 this figure of 1771 tons + 13 hundredweights had been miscopied in many accounts. Several of the guidebooks to the district were recording it as weighing 1991 tons (but still + 13 hundredweights!) Naturally this higher figure soon became rounded up in many descriptions to 'approximately', 'almost' or 'nearly' 2000 tons. Since 1799 there is no record of anyone else ever measuring the Stone, so this figure of almost 2000 tons has been perpetuated in all accounts.

In November 2001 the author and a colleague re-measured the Stone to check on the Pocklington figures. Using simple surveying tapes and measuring several cross sections of the Stone in various directions, a reasonable estimate of the volume of the stone was calculated. The specific gravity of the rock was determined as 2.65. The recalculated total weight was 1253 tons (1273 tonnes), some 518 tons lighter than Pocklington's original figure.

TOURISM

At the turn of the Eighteenth Century Pocklingon had seen that the Bowder Stone had tourist appeal. Taking his friends and guests by carriage down the rough track into Borrowdale to view the scenic wonders and be received by his lady resident at Bowderstone Cottage became a highlight of the tourist round. The Bowder Stone remained firmly established as a tourist station throughout the Victorian era and well into the Twentieth Century. As late as the inter-war years of the 1920's and 1930's Bowderstone Cottage still functioned as a tea room and souvenir shop to refresh the tens of thousands of people who every year made the walk up to the Stone and ventured to the top by the ladder. Every guide book referred to the Stone, photographic images of it appeared in all the tourist literature and to this day the Stone remains an icon of the Borrowdale valley.

Bowderstone Cottage in the 1920's, Open for Refreshments.

Records of who was the lady resident first installed by Pocklington are scanty, as are references of how this tradition was carried on. When William Green compiled his *Tourists New Guide* to the Lakes in 1819 he recorded -

This house is the summer's residence of John Raven, who, on the traveller's appearance commences an exordium preparatory to the presentation of a written paper, specifying the weight and dimensions of the stone, of which, in some seasons, he makes a profitable trade. John is a hardy man; for, in the severest weather, though more than eighty years of age, he exposes his bare scalp, and the silver grey hairs which scantily supply its borders, while on the watch for customers. His hardness of hearing makes it impossible to communicate anything to him but by means of pantomime. The movement of the hand towards the pocket, is an act John understands as well as any member of the fraternity to which he belongs.

This miserable man, blind to all the charms of surrounding nature, and to all nature's images, excepting that of the King, can have few enjoyments, being generally left alone in the house, even at night. In the day time, during business hours, the stone is visited by two young women, who are hardly more competent to furnish useful information than their grandsire.

After John Raven's time at Bowderstone Cottage, ladies again took over the role of guides. Copies of Posters advertising the Stone, mainly from the Victorian period are still in existence. Two well publicised lady guides were Mary Caradus in the 1830's and Mary Thompson, who was resident there for over 25 years from the 1850's.

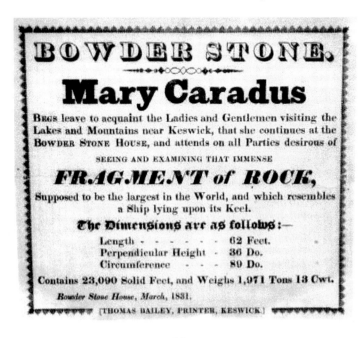

Countless tales of tourist visits to the Stone must exist. Nancy Price in *A Vagabond's Way, haphazard wanderings in the fells,* published in 1914 recounts a story that probably relates to Mary Thompson and conveys what life at Bowderstone Cottage must have been like:

> This old lady is always ready for you with pen and ink for your valued autograph. I should think she will want a special cottage to keep her ponderous tomes, if she asks everybody who pays the stone a visit for "theear writin" as she calls it. I asked her if she had any interesting autographs.
>
> "Aye, Ah cudna tell 'ee, " she said, "fur Ah canna reed".
>
> I was at a loss to think why she kept her book at all, until she went on to say: "Bit most fwoaks like writn theear names I' beuks".
>
> After you have written in your best style you give her "a trifle". She deserves it, for we must not forget the steps, and there are few who do not mount them, and thus stand majestically on top of the stone with little or no effort. She is responsible for them, and I should think by this time she has made a good profit out of her idea. As she tells you.
>
> "Ah thowt ta mysen, theear's a menny wud like to stand on't stone as cud nivver climb't, an that's ow Ah coom ta think o' steps. Whin yan lot wears oot, Ah just sets annuther oop".

"Aye, Ah thowt o' em mysen, an paid fur em mysen, seah noo Ah can set an enjy' em mysen".

There she is wiser than most financiers. To "set an enj'y" is beyond them. She is a contented old lady, but nevertheless looks older than her 75 years. Her face is the colour of a tallow candle, and is furrowed with countless wrinkles; she has the vague, far away look in her grey eyes, which is peculiar to them that live on seas or mountains.

She asked me into her cottage. There was more than one fine oak chest, and everything was clean and bright, as are most of these Cumberland cottages. She pointed to an easy chair by the fire, which was crackling merrily in defiance of sun and calendar.

"Set thee doon an hav wee bit crack"

"Aye, Ah canna git t' kirk noo, bit Ah dinna think t'Lord minds aboot gain't buildins ower much. T brings Im near enow ta set an leak t' fells"

A neighbour of hers had been reading the Bible. I told her to read on, and she did. I remember well the last words, "Lo, I am with you always, even unto the end of the world".

"Aye" said the old womwn, " doan't reed nea mair. Ah like 't ta end theear. The canna feel lonesome thinking o' them words."

It was certainly Mary Thompson that witnessed another event at the Stone in 1878. The local newspaper, *The English Lakes Visitor and Keswick Guardian* for Saturday, January 5th, of that year recorded that:

"The Derwentwater Fife and Drum Band - the members of this band, under the tuition of Mr. Thos. Atkinson, have made good progress and been very liberally encouraged this Christmas, both for their playing and exemplary conduct. When in Borrowdale they were allowed to go on the top of the Bowder Stone, and when all were comfortably seated they played 'John Peel' to the delight of the old lady who has charge of the stone, who said it was the first time a band of music had ever been on the Bowder Stone, and wished them all a Happy New Year".

It does'nt record how many were in the band!

By 1900 William Weightman, who was also the road foreman in Borrowdale ran Bowderstone Cottage.

THE STONE

The Stone is lying along its long axis and is orientated almost exactly north-south. Its maximum length is 18.65m. When viewed from the southern end (the familiar view as seen in most pictures and on the cover of this booklet) it is almost, but not exactly, square in cross section. In fact it is rather like a slightly squashed diamond. The other (northern) end is a little more irregular, but it retains the basic diamond shape. The four faces of this diamond shape are the joint planes in the lava of which it is composed - that is the cracks that appeared in the volcanic lava when it cooled.

Most of the northern half of the Stone is supported on a base or keel about 3m wide at ground level. At the southern end the keel is much narrower, thus emphasising the poised nature of the whole thing. Projecting the linear undersides downwards suggests the base of the Stone is not much more than a metre below present ground level at that end.

The weight of the Stone is fairly symmetrically distributed along the north-south centre line running directly down the centre of the base. Hence the Stone is quite stable in its present position.

The plan view shows the position of the hole enlarged by Pocklington under the keel.

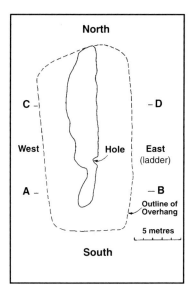

SITE PLAN

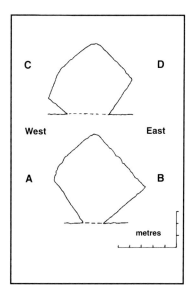

CROSS SECTIONS

13

ORIGIN OF THE STONE

No surviving legends from Lakeland folklore seem to have attached themselves to the Bowder Stone. Conjecture as to its origin has always revolved around natural geological activity even a few of these ideas being somewhat farcical.

Only two possible origins can be seriously considered. Either it was transported to its present position by ice (an erratic boulder) or, that it is a large piece of rock that fell from the crags above. Arguably there is a third possibility in a combination of these two ideas, that is, it fell from the crags onto ice and was then gradually lowered into place as the ice melted away.

AN ERRATIC BOULDER?

There have been serious suggestions that ice from Scotland brought the Stone here. Such an idea can be quickly dismissed as the Stone is undoubtedly a piece of Lake District volcanic rock and apart from that, there is absolutely no evidence anywhere that ice from Scotland ever penetrated the central Lake District. To do that it would have had to push **up** the Borrowdale valley, an idea for which there is no evidence whatsoever.

GEOLOGY

The stone is a large piece of fine grained, dark greenish-grey, andesite lava.

It is of Ordovician age and belongs to the Borrowdale Volcanic Group of rocks.

Stratigraphically it is part of the Grange Crag Member of the Birker Fell Formation, which lies close to the base of the Borrowdale Volcanic Group.

No age determinations have been carried out on this particular formation but the most recent measurements on the Borrowdale Volcanic Group as a whole give an age of around 452 million years.

Two major vertical joint planes exist in these lavas on Bowder Crag, intersecting at 85 and 95 degree angles. These determine the planar faces of the Stone.

Ice coming **down** Borrowdale from the central Lakeland Fells however, could clearly have brought such a boulder. There is ample evidence that the Lakeland Fells were heavily affected by ice in the period we loosely call the Ice Age - geologically the Pleistocene Period from approximately 2.4 million years ago to about 10,000 years ago. During that time ice was active in a series of cold phases. Ice probably buried most of the Lakeland Fells and a large valley glacier filled Borrowdale.

When we look at this possibility of ice transporting the Stone in more detail however, it becomes less and less likely. If that had been the case, the Stone would have shown some evidence of glacial transport - scratching by ice, or some abrasion or rounding - but this is not found. Just up valley of the Stone is the heavily ice scoured spur of Andersonband Crag (NY 255163) which stands well above and 'in the way' of ice bringing a boulder to this position. If ice had carried a boulder from upper Borrowdale it would have had to carry it over and slightly around this spur and then immediately deposit it. The section of the Borrowdale valley where the Bowder Stone lies is known as 'The Jaws of Borrowdale', that is, a distinctly narrow, confined section of the valley. In such situations glaciers tend to accelerate and hence it would have been more likely the ice would have carried a large boulder through this constriction rather than deposit it. Furthermore, the Jaws section does not have a significant number of erratic boulders in it. Finally, if it was an erratic from upper Borrowdale, it would have to match the rocks there.

A ROCK FALL?

The evidence that the Stone arrived at its present position as a result of a massive rock fall is overwhelming. In order to appreciate this, we must look not just at the Stone, but also consider where the stone lies and the form and nature of the steep slopes above it.

The Stone lies on a rocky platform at about 110m OD. Approximately 40m below the Stone, the River Derwent runs through a rocky defile as it passes through this narrow 'Jaws of Borrowdale' section of the valley. Above it is a steep slope surmounted by Bowder Crag, above which, lies the summit of Kings How (392m). The Stone undoubtedly came from Bowder Crag as a result of a catastrophic rock failure.

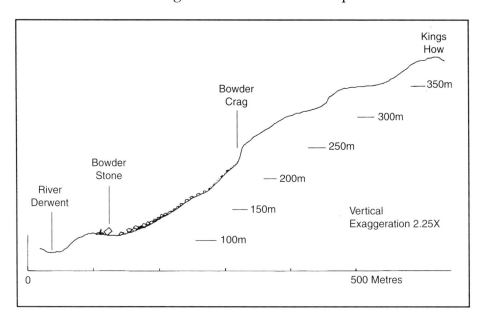

A number of reasons confirm this view:

• The rock (andesite lava) of the Stone and the material in the Hells Wall section of Bowder Crag are identical.

• The basic 'diamond' cross-sectional shape of the Stone mirrors exactly the strong vertical pattern of joints seen in the rocks of Bowder Crag. Two sets of joints running near to north-south (bearing 350 degrees) and near west-east (bearing 85 degrees) cut through these rocks. This joint pattern means that the rocks that fall from these crags all tend to have a characteristic parallelogram (diamond shaped) cross section.

• On part of the Hells Wall section of Bowder Crag the rocks also have some distinct cleavage structures (i.e. they are cut through with fine planes showing that they have been subjected to intense pressure in the past). These same structural features can be seen on the two very large standing stones which lie alongside the Stone on its western side and at some stage broke off the main part. (A and B on photograph below).

View of Stone from North End.

• At its northern end the keel of the Stone is actually broken. Two large wedges of rock at the base have fractured from the main mass but have remained in position. Fracturing would be likely in a rockfall situation, whereas if the Stone had been transported here by ice, fractured sections like this would most probably have become detached.

• The Stone is merely just one of many thousands of boulders that lie on this slope below Bowder Crag. It is undoubtedly the largest, but many others, which are close to it in size, are shown on the sketch map on page 18.

• Lastly the position of the Stone at the **foot** (or toe) of this slope below Bowder Crag is exactly where you would expect the largest pieces from a rockfall to be found. A process called **fall sorting** occurs in such situations. The largest blocks have the greatest success in overcoming frictional loss as they travel downslope. Conversely immediately below Bowder Crag the debris lying on the slopes at the top tends to be of relatively smaller size.

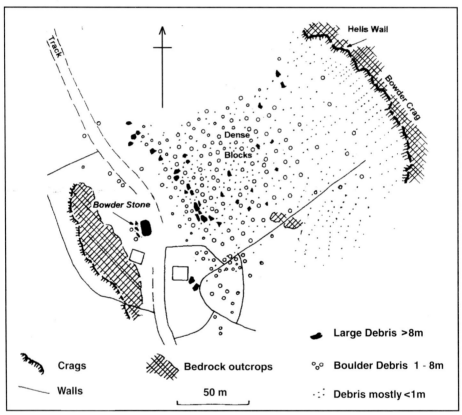

Sketch Map of the Area of the Rockfall.

Most of the very large blocks lie at the foot of the slope. Material is not being added to this lower area at the present time. Blocks continue to fall and pull away from Bowder Crag, but mostly remain high on the scree slopes.

THE EVENT

Putting all this evidence together let us try to reconstruct this rockfall event and try to visualise what is likely to have happened on that day when the Bowder Stone came down from Bowder Crag. Most probably we must be looking at a single catastrophic rock failure of the Crag, when in total, tens of thousands of tons of rock material broke away and cascaded down the slope.

The strong vertical joint planes in the rock of Bowder Crag (the planes produced by cooling when the lava flow came to rest following volcanic eruption back in the Ordovician Period of geological time) are the lines along which the rock would break. Weathering, water seepage and frost action would all be concentrated along these lines of weakness. Examination of the faces of Bowder Crag today shows deep clefts along these joint planes and huge slabs of rock pulling away from and becoming dislodged from their original position. These joints are vertical, or near vertical, in the Crag. The piece of this Crag that became the Bowder Stone is now lying on it side. You would not expect a detached piece originally 18+ m high and around 8+ m wide to end up at the foot of the slope still in a vertical position. As it fell away, it would quickly fall on to its side and would most likely have rolled sideways, bouncing and tumbling downslope.

The Bowder Stone is the largest surviving lump that reached the bottom of the slope. Many other very substantial pieces also came down with it, many of them breaking and smashing up as they crashed against each other. The size of the Bowder Stone gave it the maximum forward momentum. As it reached the foot of the slope, around 150m below, it met the slightly rising ground of the rocky platform on which it now rests and its progress would have been checked. It is likely other smaller blocks were close to it and a few may have been ahead of it. As it crashed on to this rocky protuberance tangling up with debris around it, its forward motion was stopped. It impacted with sufficient force to cause material to break off the Stone, in particular, two very large flat slabs of rock spalled off and came to rest as erect stones on the western (downslope) side (A and B on the photograph on page 17). The forward motion having been checked and substantial pieces discarded, the remaining stone gently settled backwards and, because of its symmetrically disposed weight, came to rest on its corner in a mass of smaller debris around it.

When did this large rockfall take place and why did it happen ?

In reality we have no accurate means of answering either of these questions with real certainty.

There is no evidence that it came down in historic times. If so, a major rockfall of this magnitude would have been recorded in some way or other. If the mass of boulder debris, lying on the lower part of the slopes above and around the Stone, is examined it is all completely stable at present. The boulders are heavily encrusted with lichens and mosses. In recent years dense scrubby woodland has colonised most of the area. Rock material is not being added to the lower part of the slope. Even though rocks still become dislodged and periodically fall from Bowder Crag, few reach any distance downslope. The fallen debris at the foot of the slope appears to have been there for a considerable time.

The most likely time for the fall was at the end of the last period of glaciation in the valley, or in the period immediately following. We have conclusive evidence that ice, which completely filled the Borrowdale Valley in the final phase of the Pleistocene glacial period (The Devensian as it is termed by geologists) had melted away leaving the valley ice free by 13,500 years ago. The landscape at the time, newly emerged from beneath an ice sheet and glaciers, would have been devoid of vegetation with much of the bedrock shattered and broken by frost and ice action. After something like 2,500 years of a relatively milder climate (but still cold), the area plunged once again into near glacial conditions. Between 11,000 and 10,000 years ago (the period geologists call The Loch Lomond Stadial), ice returned to some of the higher ground in the central Lake District, with thin glaciers extending down the upper Borrowdale Valley probably as far as Rosthwaite - only 2 kms away from the Bowder Stone. Thus in this time between 13,500 and 10,000 years ago Bowder Crag would most likely have been under constant frost and rainwater attack. It would have been a Crag that ice action earlier in the Pleistocene had scraped and steepened and because of its strong vertical joint structure left vulnerable to slope failure. The fall most likely occurred in this period.

THE NAME

Most probably, the name *Bowder Stone* is simply a local dialectic way of referring to a 'boulder'.

There is a suggestion that a possible derivation of its name is from Balder, one of the sons of Odin, but there is little to substantiate this.

Older accounts record a variety of different spellings. In 1772 William Gilpin in his *Observations relating to Picturesque Beauty* used *Boother-stone.*

Hutchinson in his *History of the County of Cumberland* in 1792 refers to it as *The Bowdar Stone.* A few years later James Clarke in his *Survey of the Lakes of Westmorland, Cumberland and Lancashire* used *Powder Stone* or *Bounder Stone.* Joseph Pocklington in his notebook referred to the place as *The Bowtherstone.* A further variation **Bowdore Stone** appears in an account of *A Fortnight' Ramble to the Lakes in Westmorland, Lancashire and Cumberland in 1792.*

A modern usage of the single word *Bowderstone* has recently started appearing. The National Trust now use it for their car park sign and it is also current in many of the climbing club guides to the area.

CLIMBING AND BOULDERING

As you walk up to the Bowder Stone from the car park, you are sure to notice the large abandoned Quay Foot Quarry on your left at the start of the path. This was the source of some good building stone, most of which went to build Keswick in the second half of the Nineteenth Century and the early years of the Twentieth. The material was the so-called 'Lakeland Green Slate' (actually a volcanic ash) which provided both walling and roofing material. In this particular quarry much of the 'slate' had a spotted appearance and is frequently referred to as 'rainspot slate'. At the far end of this quarry special access has now been provided for rock climbing, one of the old quarry faces is used as an abseiling face by groups of disabled people.

Further along the path there are some other prominent climbing crags on the left. You will frequently see groups of young people here being instructed in the techniques of rock climbing.

Bowder Crag is an important climbing face for experienced climbers. The smooth rock faces, pinnacles and deep crevices in the Crag provide 27 separately listed routes, some of them modern test pieces, particularly in the part known as Hells Wall.

The Bowder Stone itself is a classic site nowadays for the modern sport of 'bouldering'. You will frequently see climbers here attempting various feats of rock agility. In dry weather the chalk marks left in the climbers hand holes are often still visible, particularly on the undersides of the Stone. The Stone provides some of the hardest, low altitude bouldering in the Lake District. The Fell and Rock Climbing Club Guides of the English Lake District lists around 18 different manoeuvres on the Stone, most with highly descriptive names such as *'Picnic Sarcastic'*, *'Coming up for Air'* or *'Lateral Gruntings'*. Most of these involve contortionist movements up the southern face, or up and over the overhangs below the ladder.

Many of the routes on the ladder wall of the Stone finish once the lip of the overhang is reached, thus leaving the vegetation on the top undisturbed.

The Stone from the Ladder (Eastern) Side

Acknowledgements:

I am indebted to the staff of the Keswick Museum and Art Gallery, The Cumbria Record Office in Carlisle and the City Library in Carlisle for their help with the research. Those institutions have kindly allowed reproduction of some of the older pictures in this booklet. The modern pictures and the diagrams are all the authors. I would like to acknowledge the help of Ray Trickey with some of the field work and thank all the people of Keswick who responded to my local appeal for information on this site.

THE AUTHOR Dr. Alan Smith is now retired from an academic career in Higher Education. He has written several papers, books and guides on Lakeland Geology and is currently President of the Cumberland Geological Society. He lives in Keswick.